PUT YOUR HANDPRINT HERE.

PUT YOUR FOOTPRINT HERE.

MY SESAME STREET® YEARBOOK

Featuring Jim Henson's Sesame Street Muppets

1985

ME

MY FAVORITE PEOPLE

MY FAVORITE PLACES

MY FAVORITE TIMES

Written by
Dina Anastasio

Illustrated by
Richard Brown

Children's Television Workshop

M^E

Hey everybody, Big Bird's my name.
Does your name sound at all the same?
I like to sing. Do you sing too?
I sure would like to sing with you.
Do you wish that you could fly?
Do you ever laugh or cry?
This book is yours. I'm in it, too.
There's things to write, and things to do.
So let's begin. We'll start right here,
And keep on going through the year.

Paste a photo of yourself here.

ME, MYSELF, AND I

Does your shirt say something on it? If it does, write it on this shirt.

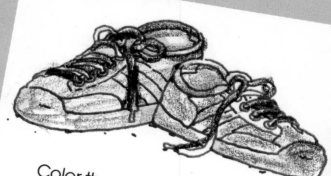

Color these sneakers the same color as your sneakers.

Write your name on this hat.

Write the name of your favorite book.

Write about some of your other favorite things here.

KITT CAR - MICHAEL KNIGHT -
MEMORY GAME - SANDY THE DOG -
COLORING WITH CRAYONS - WATCHING
SESAME STREET - READING BOOKS -
PLAY RECORDS WITH MOMMY - LOVES TO
MAKE FROSTY THE SNOWMAN

THE WAY I FEEL

When I fall down, I feel sad. What makes you feel sad?

Write about it here.

IF I GET AN SORE; - When I think ABOUT MY BROTHER JOEY THAT DIED,

When my mommy tickles me, it makes me laugh and I feel happy.

What makes you happy?

GROVER, ERNIE AND BERT, JORDAN, BUILDING BLOCKS WITH DADDY, SANDY THE DOG, M+M's CANDY, READING BOOKS COLORING, PLAYING HE-MAN PLAYING WITH JORDAN When DADDY COMES HOME

When Ernie and I have a fight, I feel angry.

What makes you feel angry?

IF JORDAN TAKES my TOYS, IF JORDAN gets into my CRAYONS, When my TOYS BREAK, When I COLOR SLOPPY, When mom AND DAD LEAVE ME WITH A SiTTER.

When I put my socks on my hands, I feel silly.

When do you feel silly?

SANDY, MY STUFFED DOGGIE, FLINTSTONES, When DADDY TiCKLES ME, WHEN JORDAN MAKES FUNNY FACES

5

THESE THINGS ARE MINE

I, furry little Grover, love my toy guitar. It is my favorite toy because it is blue like me. I like teddy bears because they are furry like me.

Do you have a teddy bear? Color this bear the same color as your bear.

Do you have toys that look like the other things on this page? If you do, color them the same colors as your toys. If you don't, color them any color you would like.

KiTT

I WISH

I sure wish that I could fly. What do you wish that you could do?

Write about it here. "FLY"
PLAY MEMORY

Gee, I wish that my rubber duckie could talk to me. Do you have something that you wish could talk to you?

Write about it here. What would it say?

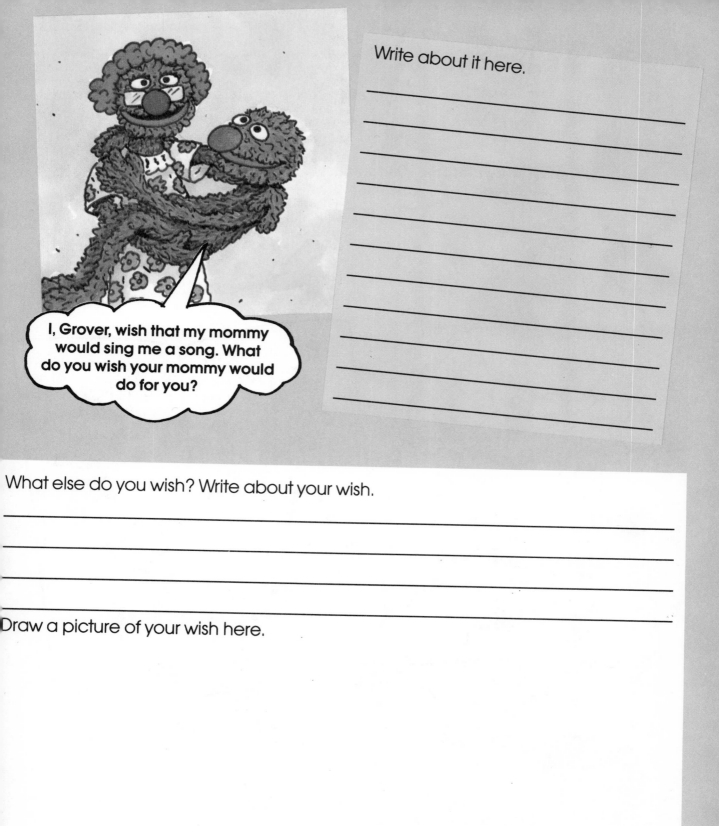

Write about it here.

What else do you wish? Write about your wish.

Draw a picture of your wish here.

FOOD FOR THOUGHT

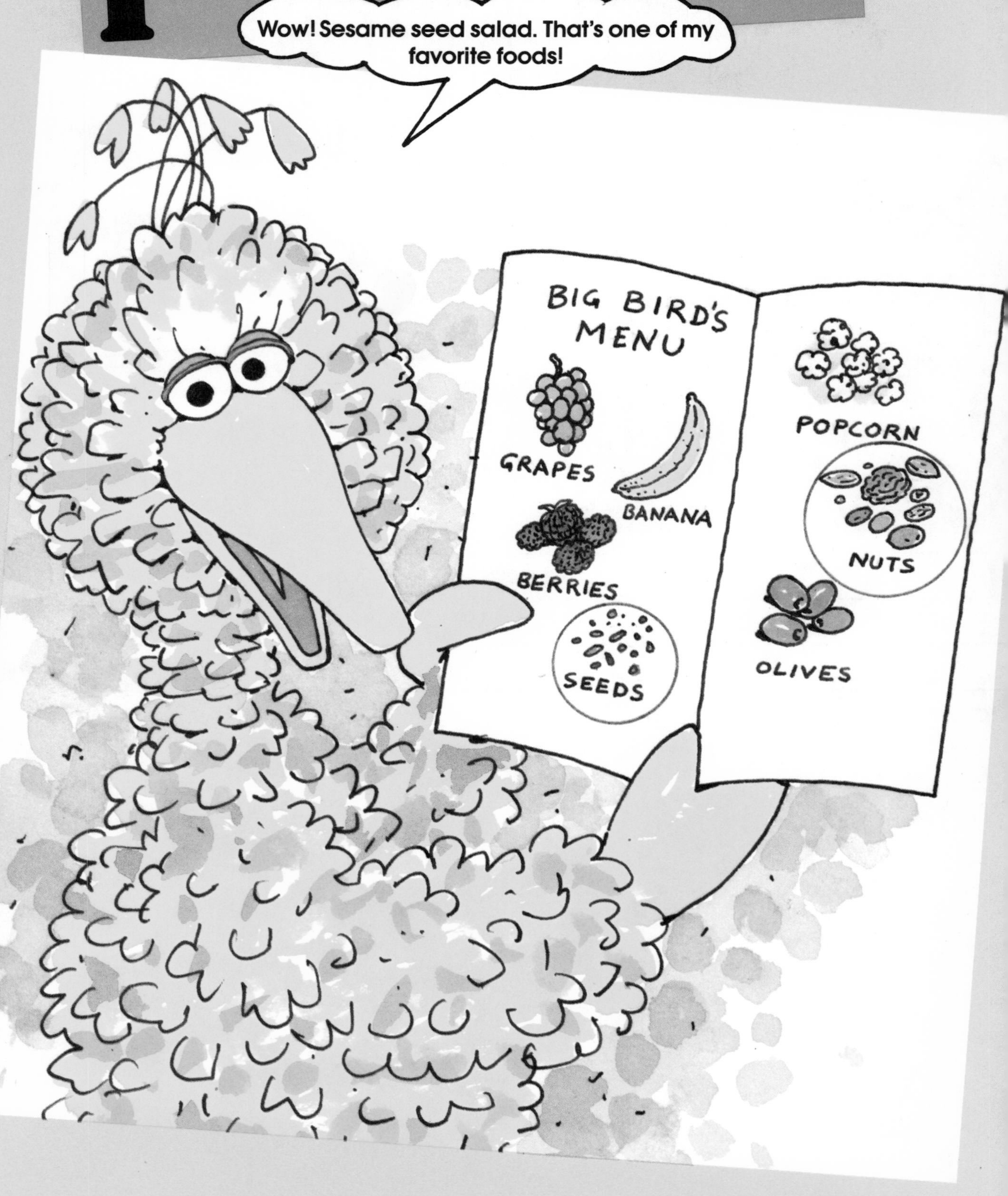

Big Bird drew circles around foods he likes to eat.
Why don't you draw circles around your favorite foods?

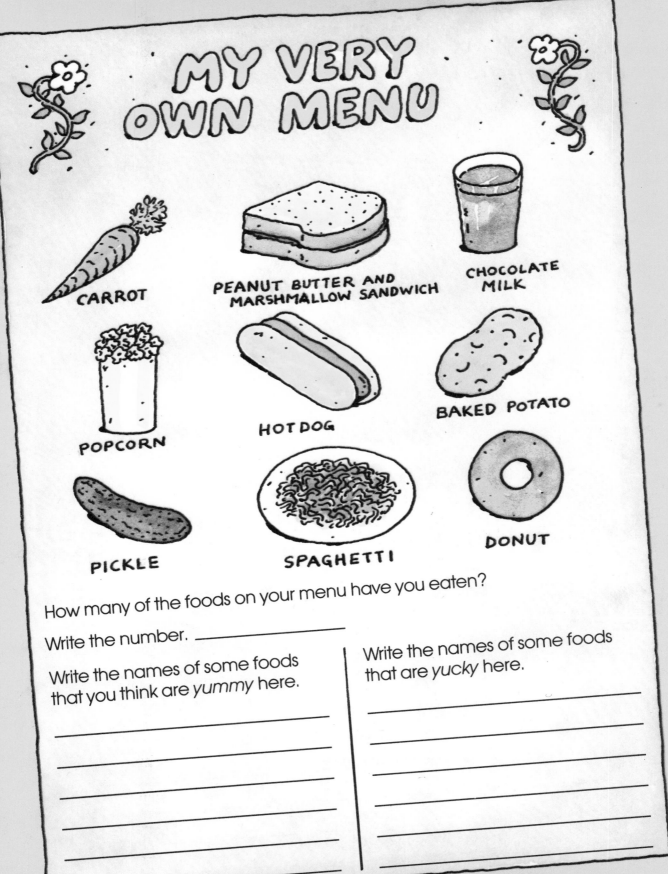

MY VERY OWN MENU

CARROT

PEANUT BUTTER AND MARSHMALLOW SANDWICH

CHOCOLATE MILK

POPCORN

HOT DOG

BAKED POTATO

PICKLE

SPAGHETTI

DONUT

How many of the foods on your menu have you eaten?

Write the number. _____

Write the names of some foods that you think are *yummy* here.

_____
_____
_____
_____

Write the names of some foods that are *yucky* here.

_____
_____
_____
_____

THIS IS ME

Draw a picture of yourself here.

Are you your favorite person? Write about yourself here.

_____

_____

_____

_____

_____

_____

_____

_____

MY FAVORITE PEOPLE

Hello everybodee, if I could talk to you,
I would talk about my family, and all my good friends too.
My mommy is the nicest mommy that I know.
Ooooh she is so smart and nice. I, Grover, love her so.
I have a friend named Ernie. He is so good to me.
Sometimes we jump. Sometimes we run. Sometimes we count to 3.
I like to sing with Big Bird. I like to read with Bert.
They are so very nice to me when I am feeling hurt.
I, furry little Grover, would like to know if you
Have lots of favorite people who are nice and loving too.

Paste a photo of one of your favorite people here.

THE PEOPLE IN MY FAMILY

Write the names of the people in your family on the lines. Draw lines from the names of the people in your family to the things that are true about them.

_____

_____

_____

_____

_____

wakes me up in the morning.

bakes me cookies.

goes in the bathroom first.

wants to play with my toys.

sits beside me at dinner.

hugs me when I'm sad.

watches TV with me.

is mean to me.

tells me to put my toys away.

tells me silly jokes.

fixes my boo boos.

tries to find me when I'm hiding.

tucks me in.

Write something about each of the other people in your family here.

_____

_____

_____

_____

_____

_____

_____

_____

I'M TALLER THAN YOU!

On the first day of school, Big Bird and a friend lined up for the school bus. They were way at the end.

Big Bird is taller than Bert. Do you know someone who is taller than you are? Write that person's name here. _____

Betty Lou is shorter than Ernie. Do you know someone who is shorter than you are? Write the name.

_____

16

Betty Lou and Prairie Dawn are the same size. Who is the same size as you are? Write the name.

_____

Oscar is grouchy. Do you know someone who is grouchy? Write the name.

_____

Ernie's T-shirt has stripes. Who has a striped T-shirt? Write the name.

_____

The friend on Big Bird's shoulder is little. Do you have a friend who is little? Write the name.

_____

Do you have a friend who is big? Write the name.

_____

BE MY VALENTINE

Who would you like to send each of these valentines to?
Write the name of a friend under each poem.

You taught me how to count
and write.
Sometimes you read to me
at night.

DADDY

We used to talk and play
all day,
But now you live real far
away. YAYIA

You are my friend.
You live nearby.
Sometimes you're nice.
Sometimes you're shy.

A DAY TOGETHER

Write a word on each line.

If I could share a special day,
I'd share it with a friend.
I think I'd call my buddy _____.
Oh what a day we'd spend!

I think we'd share a hiding place,
Behind a _____ or chair,
And if we broke my favorite _____,
I really wouldn't care.

We'd share a snack of milk and
_____.
And then we'd rest awhile.
We'd share a joke about a _____.
And that would make us smile.

When it was time for _____ to go,
We'd share a hug or two,
And then I'd say, "I'm glad that I
Could share this day with you."

20

Draw 3 wonderful things that you would like to share with the Count.

WELCOME BERT AND ERNIE

Write a word on each line.

If Bert and Ernie came to my house, I would open the door and say, "Come in and meet my _____." I would ask them if they would like to play with some of my favorite toys, like my _____ _____ and my _____, and then I would ask them if they would like to eat some _____. There are some things that I don't like other people to play with, like my _____ _____ and my _____, so I might not let them play with them, even though I like Bert and Ernie a lot.

If Bert and Ernie came to my house, I would tell them my favorite joke about _____, and then I would read them my book about _____. I would ask Ernie if he would like to wear my _____ for a while, and I would ask Bert if he would like to share my _____.

If Bert and Ernie came to my house, I would tell them about the time I laughed because _____, and the time I cried because _____. I would tell them about some of the things that scare me, like _____ and _____, and then I would ask them if anything ever scared them. I would show Ernie the things that I play with when I take a bath, like my _____ and my _____, and I would show Bert my collection of _____.

If Bert and Ernie came to my house, I would ask them to come back the next day to play a game of _____ and to meet my friend _____. And when they were gone, I would call up _____ _____ and talk about the nice day that I spent with Bert and Ernie.

This story was written by _____.

(Write your name.)

23

WHEN I GROW UP

When I grow up, I think I'd like to be a clown. What would you like to be when you grow up?

Draw a circle around each person you'd like to be when you're older.

DOCTOR

TEACHER

CHEF

DANCER

POLICE OFFICER

FIRE FIGHTER

ASTRONAUT

MY FAVORITE PERSON

PERSON OF THE YEAR

Draw a
picture of
one of your
favorite people
here.

Do you have some other favorite people?   Write their names here.

_____

_____

_____

_____

MY FAVORITE PLACES

When things are much too quiet, when everything looks fine,
I'm glad that I can hide inside a favorite place of mine.
When everything is noisy, and everything looks bad,
I'm glad that I can raise the lid, and yell and get real mad.
When somebody is singing, and I wish he'd go away,
I'm glad I have a place that I can grouch away the day.
When I need to do some thinking, I'm so glad that I'm inside.
When you need to do some thinking, do you have a place to hide?
Do you have a place that's special—or maybe you have two,
Where you can laugh or cry or sing, or just like being you?

Paste a photo of your favorite place here.

SCHOOL DAYS

On my first day of school, I, furry little Grover, was sooo happy because I used all these new things.

Draw a circle around each thing on Grover's desk that you use in school. Write on the lines.

My teacher's name is _____.

The best thing in school is _____.

The worst thing about school is _____.

These are the pets we have in school: _____.

I learned to sing a song in school. The name of it is _____.

I usually sit beside _____.

These are some other things I learned in school: _____
_____.

Did you draw a picture in school? Tape it here.

EVERYTHING IN ITS PLACE

"Hey Bert, I thought this hammock was *our* very favorite place. I haven't been in it once. Bert, hey Bert! Wake up Bert."

Do you put things in any of the places you see here?
If you do, write what is in each one.

TRUNK

DRAWER

_____
_____
_____

_____
_____
_____
_____

TOOL BOX

JEWELRY BOX

_____
_____
_____
_____

BIRD CAGE

PURSE

_____
_____
_____
_____

_____
_____
_____
_____

THROUGH YOUR WINDOW

What do you see when you look out of your window in the morning?
Draw it here.

What do you see when you look out of your window at night?
Draw it here.

Draw a circle around each place that you visited.
Draw a line under each place that you would like to visit.

If you got any tickets this year, tape them in the empty spaces. Write the name of each place you visited on the line below your ticket.

_____

_____

_____

Do you have a favorite place?
Write about it here.

What do you like to do in your favorite places?
Draw lines from the things you like to do to the places where you like to do them.

read a book

in my closet

eat popcorn

in a great big chair

hide

under a tree

take a nap

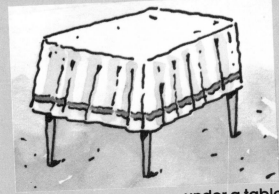
under a table

FROM HERE TO THERE

Greetings, friends. It is I, Count Von Count. How would you like to take a walk with me through your marvelous neighborhood?

But before you start, you will have to write the names of some people you know on each of these houses. Then you have to choose a path through the neighborhood. I've started without you, so you'd better hurry. Don't forget, you can visit any stores or any houses that you'd like.

Now let's count the stores. Write the number._____
How many houses are in the picture? Write the number._____
Do you know the names of any of the stores in your neighborhood?
Write them here.

_____

_____

Who do you know that lives in your neighborhood?
Write their names here.

_____

_____

MY FAVORITE PLACE

Draw a picture of your favorite place here.

What do you like to do in your favorite place?

_____

_____

_____

_____

MY FAVORITE TIMES

Bert and I were talking about our favorite times—
The time we sang a counting song, the time we made up rhymes.
I remembered laughing at a very funny joke,
Bert remembered resting, and hoping no one spoke.
I remembered parties. Bert remembered trips.
We both remembered Halloween and counting paper clips.
Did you have a favorite time that happened in this year?
Did you see a rainbow or spot a tiny deer?
Did you draw a picture of a building or the sun?
Gee I like to think about the times that I had fun.

Paste a photo of your favorite time here.

BIG BIRD'S DATE BOOK

Do you know what I did last Sunday? I went for a walk with Little Bird. I did lots of other things this week, too. I remember them because I wrote them in my date book.

What did you do this week?
Write something special that happened each day.

SUNDAY _____
_____
_____
_____
_____

MONDAY _____
_____
_____
_____
_____

TUESDAY _____
_____
_____
_____

WEDNESDAY _____
_____
_____
_____

THURSDAY _____
_____
_____
_____

FRIDAY _____
_____
_____
_____

SATURDAY _____
_____
_____
_____
_____

A VERY SPECIAL PARTY

Hmmmm, something very mysterious has happened.

One day, Sherlock Hemlock came to your door and said, "Hmmmm, something very mysterious has happened. I have one party invitation left and I can't remember who it is for."

Sherlock showed you the invitation. It said, "To _____. Come to my party. From Sherlock."

"This party is today," Sherlock said. "And I need you to help me figure out who should get this invitation."

Sherlock Hemlock grabbed his magnifying glass and led you out the door. "I have one clue," he said. "I left this button next to the invitation. I know it belongs to the person I was sending the invitation to. I'm going to see if I can find the person who lost this button."

TAPE ONE OF YOUR BUTTONS HERE.

Sherlock looked at your shirt and said, "This button looks like the buttons on your shirt. Do you know where you bought it? Maybe the person we are looking for bought a shirt in the same place."

"I have a price tag," you said.

PASTE A PRICE TAG HERE.

Sherlock lead you down the street and into a store. Near the shirt counter you found a candy wrapper.

PASTE THE WRAPPER FROM YOUR FAVORITE CANDY HERE.

"Another clue," said Sherlock, looking through his magnifying glass. "Maybe the person who lost this button lost this candy wrapper, too. We had better go to the candy store and investigate."

You and Sherlock went to the candy store. Near the candy counter, he found a picture.

PASTE A PICTURE OF YOURSELF HERE.

"My, this person looks familiar. I think this person was going to get a haircut today."

You led Sherlock out of the candy store and down the street to the barber shop. He showed the picture to the barber. "Have you seen this person?" said Sherlock.

The barber looked at the picture and chuckled. "As a matter of fact, that person had a haircut this morning. You might even find some of that person's hair on the floor of my shop."

TAPE A LOCK OF YOUR HAIR HERE.

"Hmmm," said Sherlock. "A very good clue indeed. Now we know a lot about this person. Let's go back to your house and talk it over."

You and Sherlock went back to your house and opened the door. "Surprise!" shouted all your friends.

"Is this another clue?" you asked.

"It's the best clue of all," said Sherlock. "It's a surprise party for you. I knew all along who the invitation was for and now you do, too."

"Surprise!" said Sherlock. And then you both laughed.

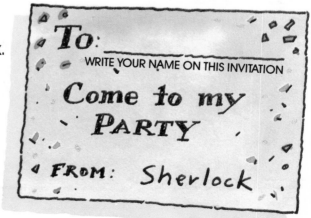

To: _____

WRITE YOUR NAME ON THIS INVITATION

Come to my PARTY

FROM: Sherlock

FUN AND GAMES

Betty Lou and Prairie Dawn like to play tag.
Who do you know that likes to do the other things on this game board?
Play this game with someone special.

START

HIDE AND SEEK

ROLLER SKATING

DROP THE HANDKERCHIEF

RING-AROUND-THE-ROSY

ICE SKATING

Cut out 4 small pieces of paper, and write a number from 1 to 4 on each one.
Then turn them over so that you cannot see the numbers.
Use a button or a penny as your playing piece.
Choose a number card and move that many spaces.

Do you know someone who likes to do that?
Write the name of that person under the picture.
Keep playing until there is a name under each picture.

BASEBALL

FOOTBALL

HOCKEY

JACKS

BOARD GAME

HAPPY BIRTHDAY

I, Sherlock Hemlock, the world's greatest detective, have found lots of things that are missing on this page.

How old were you this year? Draw that number of candles on this cake. Did you get some nice presents for your birthday? Write the name of each person who gave you a present on a tag. Then write what was in each package.

FROM GRANDMA

SCHOOL OUTFIT TOY

decorated with a fire engine truck

choclate cake from Lutz's

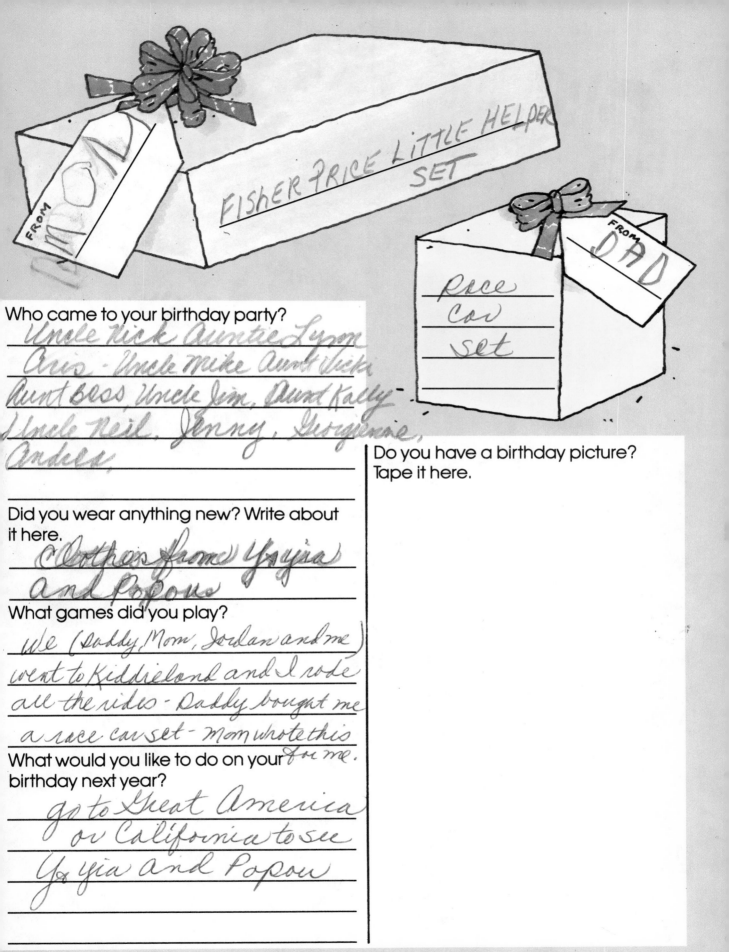

FISHER PRICE LITTLE HELPER SET

FROM MOM

FROM DAD

Race
Car
Set

Who came to your birthday party?

Uncle Nick Auntie Lynn
Chris. Uncle Mike Aunt Vicki
Aunt Bess, Uncle Jim, Aunt Kally
Uncle Neil, Jenny, Georgenne,
Andres,

Did you wear anything new? Write about it here.

Clothes from YiaYia
and Popou

What games did you play?

We (Daddy, Mom, Jordan and me)
went to Kiddieland and I rode
all the rides - Daddy bought me
a race car set - Mom wrote this
for me.

What would you like to do on your birthday next year?

go to Great America
or California to see
YiaYia and Popou

Do you have a birthday picture? Tape it here.

GROVER'S HAT

I, furry little Grover, have lost my hat.

Do you have a picture of you in your Halloween costume? If you don't, draw a picture of what you wore on Halloween. Write your name on the picture and use it in this story. Every time you come to an empty square, move your picture to it.

It was a dark, scary Halloween night, and ☐ was waiting to go trick or treating with Grover.

When Grover arrived, he looked very sad.

"What's the matter Grover?" ☐ asked.

"I, Grover, do not feel so well. I had a wonderful witch's costume, but now I have lost my hat."

"I'll help you find it," ☐ said.

Grover and ☐ walked down the street very slowly. "Did you stop anywhere?" ☐ asked.

"I stopped at one house," Grover said. "The woman gave me some candy."

On the corner, they met Ernie. Ernie was wearing a clown's costume. "Does your hat look like Ernie's?" ☐ asked.

"My hat had a point like Ernie's," Grover said. "But it was different."

Grover and ☐ stopped at a house and shouted, "Trick or treat."
The man at the door put a candy bar in each of their bags.
On the next corner, they met Betty Lou. Betty Lou was wearing a cowgirl's

costume. "Does your hat look like Betty Lou's?" ☐ asked.

"My hat had a brim like Betty Lou's," Grover said. "But it was different."

Grover and ☐ walked up to a house and rang the doorbell. A woman opened the door. When she saw Grover, she said, "Well, if it isn't the little blue witch again. I think you forgot something."

"Is this the house that you stopped at?" ☐ asked.
Grover nodded and said, "I forgot. I've been here before." Then he looked at the three pumpkins in the window. Each pumpkin was wearing a hat. There was a fire fighter's hat, a witch's hat, and a chef's hat.
"Everybody seems to be losing his hat tonight," the woman said.

"Is one of those hats yours?" ☐ asked.
Grover pointed to one of the hats. "That one is mine," Grover said.
Grover put the hat on his head and thanked the woman.

Then ☐ and Grover shouted, "Happy Halloween" and went on their way.

Tape your picture next to Grover.

Did anything else happen on your trip? Write about it here.

_____

_____

_____

_____

_____

_____

_____

I packed
8 yo-yos
in my suitcase.
What did you pack
in your suitcase?

I met
3 sad clowns.
Who did you meet?

THE BEST TIME I CAN IMAGINE

Draw a picture of your favorite time.

How do I know that Sesame Street is a wonderful show for young children?

A little bird told me!

See us every weekday on your Public Television Station.
(Check local listings for time and channel.)

MESSAGES TO ME

Ask your friends and family to write a special message to you here.